Biological
Systems

Workbook one

edexcel

advancing learning, changing lives

topic: fit and well

1: How are you?

What do people say if you ask them, "How are you?"

They might include words such as:

> fine · not well · poorly · tired · exhausted · aching
>
> ill · great · fighting fit · good · dreadful · headachy

Try it. Casually ask friends and relatives the question.

Add any other words they use:

_____

_____

How we feel depends on our physical state, mental state and general sense of well-being. How does fitness fit in? Well, health and fitness are closely linked, but they aren't the same thing.

If you're healthy you are free from disease. You are not ill.

If you're healthy you may or may not be fit.

Fitness is how well your body can perform a range of activities. World-class athletes are super fit. They perform extraordinary feats of speed, strength and endurance beyond any of us. Yet if they over-train they may weaken their immune system. This makes them more susceptible to illness.

Being fit can make you feel better, mentally and physically.

2: Fitness

We're all different. That includes how fit we are.

You can assess a person's fitness by getting them to do physical tests and measuring things such as pulse rate and lung volume.

Here are three measures of fitness (they aren't the only ones):

* **how flexible you are**
* **how quickly your pulse rate recovers after exercise**
* **how much air your lungs can hold.**

Work with partner to investigate your fitness levels.

How flexible are you?

Spend a few minutes discussing what your flexibility depends on. Write your ideas here:

_____

_____

_____

Measuring your flexibility index

Health and safety: A risk assessment must be carried out before starting work. If the participant shows any discomfort, then stop immediately. Ask a qualified person to check all PE activities before starting.

Take it in turns to be measured and take the measurements.

1   Warm up for several minutes by jogging on the spot.

2   Put a metre rule or tape measure on the floor and tape it down with masking tape or sellotape.

3   Sit on the floor with your legs either side of the metre rule so your heels are at the 50 cm mark and your knees are near the 0 cm mark. Ask your partner to hold your legs straight, but not so that they get in the way of your movements.

4   Put one hand on top of the other so that your middle fingers are lined up.

5   Now slowly stretch forward in a single movement. Do not bounce or jerk. Lean forward as far as you can, sliding your fingers along the metre rule. Stop if you feel any pain!

6   Record how far you have been able to reach down the metre rule. Take the measurement from the tip of your middle finger. This is your *flexibility index*.

7   Repeat this three more times, write your measurements in the table and calculate the mean.

Attempt	Distance reached / cm
1	
2	
3	
4	
Mean	

Results

Collect the flexibility index values from everyone in the group.

Make a table in your logbook or file. Rank the data from highest to lowest flexibility index value.

Display them using a bar chart.

The scientists

Make a list of people whose job includes measuring flexibility.

_____

_____

What do they need to know about, to help others become more flexible?

_____

_____

_____

a physiotherapist stretches a patient's shoulder

How quickly does your pulse rate recover?

When you do physical work, like running or star-jumps, your heart beats faster. How quickly it slows down, once you've stopped exercising, is another measure of fitness. The fitter you are, the quicker your pulse returns to normal. This is your **recovery time**. Fitness trainers often take these measurements.

Measuring your recovery time

Health and safety: A risk assessment must be carried out before starting work. If the participant shows any discomfort, then stop immediately. Ask a qualified person to check all PE activities before starting. Make sure no participants have a heart condition before starting the procedure.

1. Sit quietly for several minutes. Take your pulse for 15 seconds (see below). Multiply this by four to work out your pulse rate per minute. Repeat three times. Work out the mean. Put your results **table 1**.

2. Now do three minutes hard physical work. For example, star jumps, press-ups or power walking. Work up a sweat!

3. Take your pulse at one minute intervals until it has returned to its resting rate or until 10 minutes has passed.

4. Repeat the test (step 2 and 3) two more times. Put your results in **table 2**.

Taking a pulse: Turn the hand so the palm is upwards. Place your index finger and middle finger (you can use either hand) on their forearm, about 2 cm from the top of the wrist. Feel for a pulse (you will feel a throb). Apply light pressure with your two fingers. Count the number of pulses in 15 seconds.

Table 1: At rest

Heart beats in 15 seconds	Pulse rate / beats min⁻¹
1	
2	
3	
Mean	

Table 2: After exercise

Test		Time after stopping work / minutes									
		1	2	3	4	5	6	7	8	9	10
1	Pulse rate / beats min⁻¹										
2	Pulse rate / beats min⁻¹										
3	Pulse rate / beats min⁻¹										

Results

For each test, draw a line graph of your results.

Put *time* on the *x* axis and *pulse rate* on the *y* axis.

Compare your results with your partner's.

On the basis of this test, who is fitter?

Explain your answer.

_____

_____

_____

_____

_____

_____

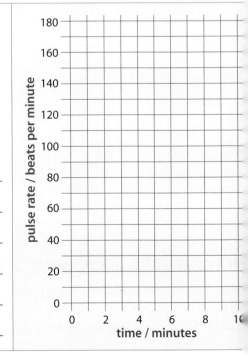

The scientists

List people who measure recovery times in their job.

_____

_____

What do they need to know about, to help others improve their recovery times?

_____

_____

_____

How much air can your lungs hold?

Having a large lung capacity means you can get lots of oxygen into your body.

Measuring the volume of air your lungs can hold

Health and safety: A risk assessment must be carried out before starting work. If the participant shows any discomfort, then stop immediately. Ask a qualified person to check all PE activities before starting. Make sure no participants have breathing problems (such as asthma or bronchitis) before starting the procedure.

You will be given various bits of apparatus:

- a 5 dm^3 graduated bottle or bell jar.
- 30-40 cm length of rubber tube and bung.
- Perspex sheet to stopper the plastic bottle while inverting it. (Alternatively, use a pump, tubing and connectors.)
- sink or large container and water supply
- disposable plastic straws and sticky tape
  [BIOHAZARD: each particpant should use a new straw].

Look at the picture. Work out how to measure the volume of the air you can breathe out of your lungs.

Make three measurements and work out the mean.

Attempt	1	2	3	mean
Volume of air breathed out / cm^3				

Results

Collect the mean volumes from everyone in the group. Record the data in your logbook or file. Draw a bar chart to display them. Who's the fittest?

The scientists

Who might want to increase their lung capacity?

Professional rowers have large lung capacities

_____

_____

What do they need to know to help increase their lung capacity?

_____

_____

3: VO2 max

VO2 max is the maximum volume of oxygen used in one minute per kilogram of body weight. It's measured in in cubic centimetres (cm^3). The higher the value, the fitter you are.

There are machines that can monitor you while you're exercising. They automatically calculate your VO2 max. Luckily, there's a simple test that doesn't use specialist equipment. It's called the Rockport Fitness Walking Test. All you need is large flat surface (such as a running track), bathroom scales and a stop watch.

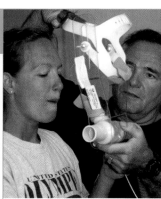

A head-set is worn while exercising. It's connected to a machine that monitors and calculates your VO2 max.

Determining VO2 max

What to do

Work with a partner to find one another's VO2 max.

Measure your partner's mass using bathroom scales.

Your mass _____ kilograms   Your partner's mass _____ kilograms

Walk one mile (1609 metres) as fast as possible, but don't run. Record the time taken.

Your time _____ minutes   Your partner's time _____ minutes

At the end of the walk, immediately take your pulse.

Your pulse _____ beats per minute   Your partner's pulse _____ beats per minute

Calculations

VO2 max =
132.853 - (0.1696 ˘ body mass in kg) - (0.3877 ˘ age in years) - (3.2649 ˘ time in mins) - (0.1565 ˘ pulse rate in beats per minute)
If you're male, add 6.315 to the value.

Your VO2 max = _____ cm^3 kg^{-1} min^{-1} Your partner's VO2 max = _____ cm^3 kg^{-1} min^{-1}

Don't worry about the units (cm^3 kg^{-1} min^{-1}). You'll learn more about units as you go through the course.

Which one of you is fitter? _____

Evaluation

The test is **reliable** if the person is walking *as fast as possible*, but not running.

Results are very close to those obtained using other methods. So, the Rockport Fitness Walking Test is **valid**.

Setting the standard

Various organisations use VO2 max when they assess fitness.

For example, the Royal Navy uses a VO2 max test. To pass, your score must be higher than these scores:

Male

Age	Under 25	Under 30	Under 35	Under 40	Under 45	Under 50
VO2 score	46.4	44.4	42.4	40.4	38.4	36.4

Female

Age	Under 25	Under 30	Under 35	Under 40	Under 45	Under 50
VO2 score	37.5	35.5	33.5	31.5	29.5	27.5

Source: http://www.royal-navy.mod.uk/server/show/nav.3520

Work in a small group to find out what fitness tests other organisations use.

Each person should take responsibility for one organisation.

You could find out about:

The fire service (www.fireservice.co.uk/fitness)

The British Army (www.armedforces.co.uk)

The RAF (www.rafcareers.com/istherafforme/requirements.cfm)

The police (www.policecouldyou.co.uk)

Summarise your group's findings on one side of A4 paper.

Improving your VO2 max

You can increase your VO2 max by:

- Exercising hard enough to get your pulse up to 65 - 85% of its previous maximum, for at least 20 minutes. Do this three to five times a week.

You could work with a group of others, to see how much you can improve your VO2 max.

Take advice on the type of exercise to carry out.

No matter how hard you train, it's unlikely you'll ever match seven-times winner of the Tour de France, Lance Armstrong. His VO2 max is 83.8.

4: Health workers

Scientists in the health industry

Many people work in the health industry. All use scientific knowledge to do their jobs effectively.

Fill in as much of the table as you can for the five health workers listed.

Add to it as you learn more.

Health worker	What they do	Science they need to know about
Doctor	_____ _____	_____ _____
Physiotherapist	_____ _____	_____ _____
Microbiologist	_____ _____	_____ _____
Nurse	_____ _____	_____ _____
Fitness trainer	_____ _____ _____	_____ _____ _____

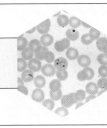

topic: heart, blood and blood vessels

1: The heart of the matter

The **heart** beats about 70 times a minute continually from before we're born to the day we die.

It's an incredibly strong muscular pump that forces blood around the body.

For the heart to pump continuously, it needs its own blood supply. This comes from the network of **coronary arteries**, which run through its muscle.

When you've learnt about the heart, label these parts of the heart on the diagram, below.

Don't forget: we label diagrams as though we're looking at a person - so the right hand side of the diagram is actually the left-hand side of the person!

A	right atrium	B	~~left atrium~~	C	~~right ventricle~~
D	left ventricle	E	~~vena cava~~	F	pulmonary vein
G	pulmonary artery	H	tricuspid valve	I	semi-lunar valves
J	valve tendons	K	~~bicuspid valve~~	L	aorta
M	muscle				

Now draw arrows on the diagram to show the direction of blood flow.

Use these labels:

- to lungs
- from lungs
- to head and body
- from head and body

Why is the wall of the left ventricle much more muscular than the right ventricle wall?

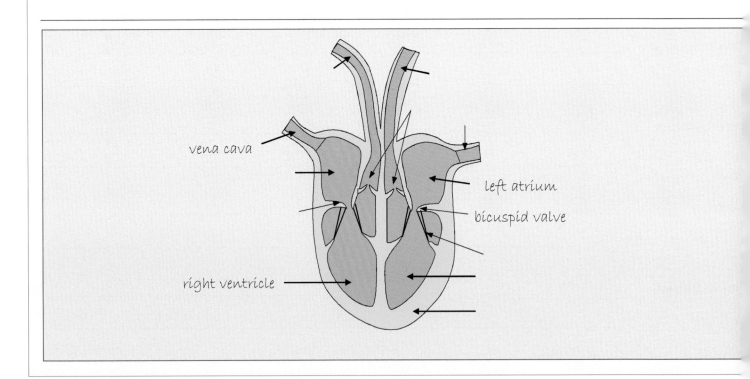

2: Blood vessels

Don't burst a blood vessel

Hundreds of tiny tubes called blood vessels carry blood around the body. Blood takes food and oxygen *to* organs and tissues and takes *away* waste products.

Cardiologists study the heart and blood vessels. They use a number of techniques to see whether our arteries and veins are healthy.

Have a look at the microscope slides of a vein and an artery. *If you're not sure how to set up and use a light microscope, there's a standard procedure on page 30 of this workbook.*

Discuss the differences between veins, arteries and capillaries. Then name and label the diagrams, right.

1   Which type of blood vessel has valves? Explain why.

_____

_____

_____

_____

2   Why do arteries have thicker walls and more muscle than veins?

_____

_____

_____

3   Is the diameter of the lumen larger in arteries or in veins? Explain why.

_____

_____

_____

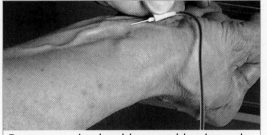

Doctors need to be able to see blood vessels so they can draw blood from patients

Name:_____

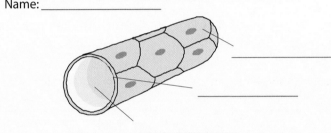

Name:_____

Name:_____

An **angiogram** is an X-ray picture of the blood vessels. It's used by surgeons to look at the flow of blood. A fine, hollow tube called a **catheter** is introduced into an artery in the forearm or groin. An X-ray opaque dye is then injected into the blood vessels and X-rays taken from several angles.

4   If the surgeon notices someone has *furred up* arteries, what does this mean?

_____

5   What might have caused the arteries to clog up?

_____

6   What might the surgeon do to treat the problem?

_____

3: Circulation

All mammals, including us, have a **double circulation** system. This means that for every time the blood passes through the body once it passes through the heart twice.

Look at the diagram, right. Put your pointing finger on the **body capillaries** and follow the arrows round until you get back to where you started.

Double circulation means that blood pressure is given a boost when the blood comes back to the heart from the lungs on its way to the body. Blood pressure always drops when blood passes through capillaries.

lung capillaries

deoxygenated blood

Heart

A B

C D

oxygenated blood

body capillaries

A = right atrium
B = left atrium
C = right ventricle
D = left ventricle

◆ = deoxygenated blood
◆ = oxygenated blood

Questions

1   Explain why the walls of the atria are thinner than the walls of the ventricles.

_____

_____

_____

2   Why is the wall of the right ventricle thinner than the wall of the left ventricle?

_____

_____

3   Why are there valves between the atria and the ventricles?

_____

_____

4   Find out what materials surgeons use when they replace heart valves.

_____

_____

5   Nurses measure blood pressure to find out about the condition of a persons' heart and blood vessels.

Think of one possible reason why a person might suffer from:

Low blood pressure:

_____

_____

High blood pressure:

_____

_____

Add other people's good ideas to your list, after they've been checked by your teacher.

4: What is blood?

Blood is very important to us as it does some very important jobs.

Fill in the blank boxes.

Blood component	Function	Explanation	Distinguishing features
Red blood cells		Oxygen binds to the red pigment haemoglobin inside the cells.	Disc shape Red (contain haemoglobin) No nucleus
White blood cells (there are different types, these are two):	Defence		
Platelets		When you cut yourself these stop the bleeding by forming jellied lumps called clots.	Very tiny granules in the plasma
Plasma		Simple chemicals dissolve in the watery plasma. Large molecules are carried in suspension.	

Looking at a blood smear

Pathologists can see whether a patient has the correct amount of each type of blood cell by looking at blood smears.

Use your microscope to look at a professionally prepared microscope slide of human blood.

If you're not sure how to set up and use a light microscope, there's a standard procedure on page 30 of this workbook.

Look for: **red blood cells** and **two different types of white blood cell** (Hint: look at the nuclei)

Make drawings of what you see.

Red blood cell

Things to label:

cell membrane • no nucleus • red haemoglobin

One type of white blood cell

Things to label:

cell membrane • cytoplasm • nucleus

Another type of white blood cell

Things to label:

cell membrane • cytoplasm • nucleus

1   What might a pathologist think if the smear shows too many white blood cells?

_____

_____

2   What could be wrong with the patient if their smear shows too few red blood cells?

_____

_____

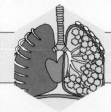

topic: lungs and respiration

1: How often do you breathe?

Your breathing rate (sometimes called **respiratory rate**) is the number of breaths you take in a minute.

A whole breath is a breath in followed by a breath out. Breathing supplies the oxygen we need and gets rid of the waste carbon dioxide we make. Oxygen reacts with food we eat, to release its energy. This energy is used by our bodies to do things such as moving and eating.

This investigation looks at whether level of activity affects breathing rate. Work in pairs. One of you will be the subject while the other takes measurements. When you've completed the activities, swap roles. Make sure your breathing returns to normal before starting each bit of exercise. Carefully read what you have to do before starting.

Breathing rate with increased levels of excercise

Health and safety: A risk assessment must be carried out before starting work. If the participant shows any signs of discomfort, then stop immediately. Ask a qualified person to check all PE activities before starting.

Carry out these three activities. After each one, your partner should count the number of breaths you take in one minute. Repeat each activity three times and work out the mean number of breaths per minute. Record your results in the table.

1   **At rest:** Sit quietly for three minutes.

2   **Mild exercise:** Walk on the spot for two minutes.

3   **Heavy exercise:** Run on the spot for two minutes.

Your results	breaths per minute			
	1	2	3	mean
At rest				
Mild exercise				
Heavy exercise				

Your partner's results	breaths per minute			
	1	2	3	mean
At rest				
Mild exercise				
Heavy exercise				

1   What is the relationship between your breathing rate and your level of activity?

_____

2   Explain why breathing rates change.

_____

_____

3   Normally, an adult breathes about 15-20 times per minute. Why is it important for a doctor or nurse to know what the normal breathing rate is?

_____

_____

Why does your heart beat faster when you do physical work?

Doing things requires energy. It comes from the food you eat.

During respiration the food reacts with oxygen to release energy. This reaction is called **aerobic respiration**.

When you do physical work:

- you use more energy
- you use more oxygen
- you need more food (glucose)
- you produce more carbon dioxide

Your blood picks up oxygen from the air you breathe into your lungs and takes it to active cells.

At the same time it removes the waste carbon dioxide that your cells make and transports it back to the lungs.

This table compares the percentages of gases in the air we breathe in with the air we breathe out:

Gas	The air we breathe in	The air we breathe out
nitrogen	78 %	78 %
oxygen	21 %	16 %
carbon dioxide	0.03 %	3 %
water vapour	small amount	significantly moist

When you've been doing hard physical activity your brain detects the extra carbon dioxide that your cells make.

High levels of carbon dioxide are toxic and must be removed.

The brain sends nerve impulses to the heart to beat faster.

This increase in heart beat rate increases blood flow.

This has three important effects.

- It takes more oxygen from the lungs **to** active cells.
- It removes more carbon dioxide **from** active cells.
- It takes more food (glucose) **to** active cells.

The lungs are made of millions of air sacs called **alveoli**.

They're specially adapted for gas exchange by:

- having a thin cell membrane
- having a very large surface area made up of individual **alveolus**
- having a very rich blood supply.

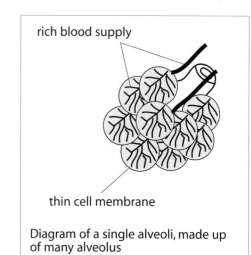

rich blood supply

thin cell membrane

Diagram of a single alveoli, made up of many alveolus

Questions

1   What do our cells need energy for?

_____

_____

2   Why is there a difference in the percentage of oxygen in the air that we breathe in compared with the air we breathe out?

_____

_____

_____

_____

2: Breathe in, breathe out!

Breathing keeps us alive! Try making the model below to show you how we breathe in and out. Before you start, read the instructions and collect the materials.

The thorax model

Health and safety: A risk assessment must be carried out before starting work.

1   Cut three pieces of plastic tubing: two short, one longer. Fit them together with a three-way connector.

2   Tape a balloon onto each short piece of tubing. Push the longer tube through a bung with a central hole. Fit the bung to the neck of the bottle. The balloons will be inside the bottle.

3   Cut the rubber sheet into a circle about 2-3 cm larger than the diameter of the bottle. Use tape or elastic bands to fix the sheet onto the open end of the bottle. Make sure the join is air-tight.

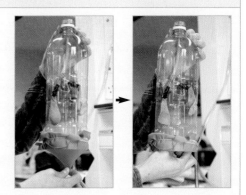

When you gently pull the rubber sheet down you should see the balloons inflate in the bottle. When you let it go the balloons should deflate again.

Compare your model with the diagram of the thorax, right.

Complete this table saying what each part of your model represents.

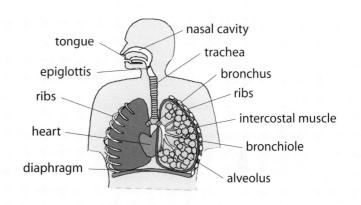

Part of model	Part in your body
Balloon	_____
Plastic tube	_____
Plastic bottle	_____
Rubber sheet	_____

Explain how your model shows what happens in the body when you breathe in and out.

_____

_____

_____

3: Gas exchange

The air we breathe in is different from the air we breathe out. (See the table on page 14.)

1   List two differences between the gases of the air we breathe in and the air we breathe out.

_____

_____

2   Why is the air we breathe out warmer than the air we breathe in?

_____

3 Why is the air we breathe out more moist than the air we breathe in?

_____

4 What difference in breathing rate would you expect to see if someone suffered from asthma?

_____

5 Imagine if your friend collapsed. They weren't breathing and their heart stopped beating. What should you immediately do, and why? When taken to hospital, which medical scientists would you expect to care for your friend? What would you expect them to do?

_____

_____

_____

_____

4: Aerobic respiration

During **aerobic respiration** your circulatory system transports food (from your intestines) and oxygen (from your lungs) to active cells where the energy is released. Energy is measured in joules (J).

Here's the equation for aerobic respiration:

glucose + oxygen → carbon dioxide + water + energy

This equation can also be written in symbols:

$$C_6H_{12}O_6 + 6O_2 \rightarrow 6CO_2 + 6H_2O + energy$$

Respiration uses glucose. But we don't eat much glucose.

Instead, our cells *convert* some of the food we eat into glucose.

Try the next experiment to see how much energy there is in sugar.

Read through the procedure. Collect the equipment you need and set up your work space neatly.

Some activities (like sleeping or just sitting quietly) use very little energy.

Others, like running around or playing sport, need much more.

How much energy is there in sugar?

Health and safety: A risk assessment must be carried out for each procedure before starting work. Wear protective clothing and eye protection. Take care when handling hot sugar.

- top-pan balance (0.1g) • deflagrating spoon (or old stainless steel tea spoon) • Bunsen burner • heat proof mat
- boiling tube • thermometer • sugar • eye protection • 20 cm³ measuring cylinder • calculator
- filter paper • test tube holder • clamp, boss and stand

1	Measure 20 cm³ of water.	4	Place a filter paper on the pan of the top pan balance.
2	Pour it into the boiling tube.	5	Press the button to zero the balance.
3	Measure its temperature and record it in the table.	6	Weigh out 1 g of sugar.

7   Place the sugar in the deflagrating spoon (or stainless steel spoon).

8   Set fire to the sugar by holding it briefly in the Bunsen flame. Use the flame to heat the water in the boiling tube (hold the tube with the test tube holder, as in the photo).

Continue until the sugar flame has burned out.

9   Record the highest temperature reached in the table.

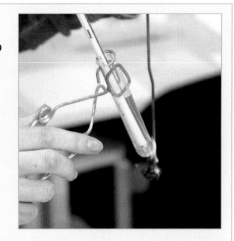

Water temperature before heating / °C	
Water temperature after heating / °C	
Temperature rise / °C	

Now do the following calculation to see how much energy was in the sugar:

Energy in 1 gram of sugar =

Volume of water / cm^3 x temperature rise x 4.2 J

[4.2 Joules are needed to raise 1 cm^3 of water by 1 °C]

Share your results with two other people in your class.

	Energy content of 1g of sugar / J
Your result	
Another result	
Yet another result	

Why is it important to get as much heat as possible from the burning sugar to heat the water in the boiling tube?

_____

_____

Why is there a difference between your result and those of the rest of the class?

_____

_____

Suggest a way you could have made your experiment better.

_____

_____

Another type of respiration

Sometimes, while you are doing a lot of very intensive activity, your lungs and blood system are not able to get enough oxygen to active cells.

As oxygen does not get to active cells fast enough for aerobic respiration they start **anaerobic respiration**.

The cells only get a little energy from glucose without using oxygen.

glucose → lactic acid + a little energy

Lactic acid builds up in your muscles and this makes them hurt.

This is called **muscle fatigue**. To get rid of the lactic acid you need more oxygen.

This extra oxygen is called the **oxygen debt**.

You have to breathe faster and more deeply, even when you've stopped exercising. The oxygen reacts with the lactic acid and breaks it down to water and carbon dioxide. Your muscles gradually hurt less.

This oxygen debt is paid.

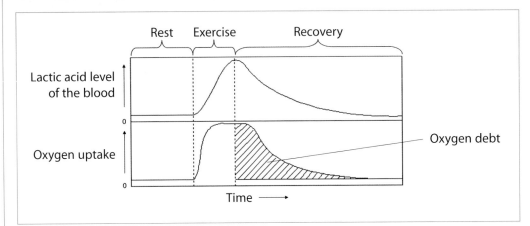

The top graph shows your lactic acid levels.

The lower graph shows how much oxygen you take into your body.

Try this ...

- Lift one arm up above your head, hold the other by your side.
- Clench and unclench your fists as quickly as you can for as long as you can. (You probably won't be able to do it for longer than a minute!)
- When you can't do it any longer rest your arm in your lap.
- Be aware of how your arms feel. It will hurt at first but then it will gradually recover.

1   Why did the arm above your head hurt?

_____

_____

2   Why did your arm stop hurting?

_____

_____

5: Health, food and diet

Look at the pictures of foods on the next page.

1   Tick the foods that you eat frequently (every day or every other day). Use a red pencil or pen for those you think are unhealthy and a green one for those that are healthy.

2   Fill in the table with your healthy and unhealthy foods.

3   Write why you think each food is healthy or unhealthy in the third column.

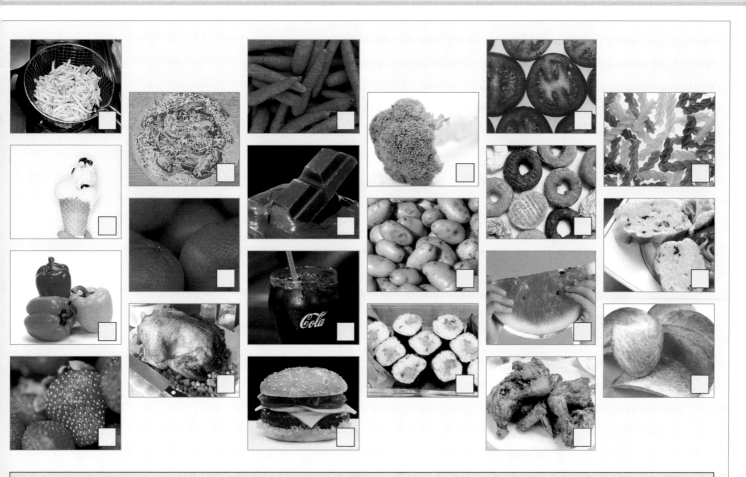

~ My diet ~		
Unhealthy food (red ticks)	**Healthy food (green ticks)**	**Reason for decision (e.g. high in salt)**

4   Suggest two long term effects of an unhealthy diet.

_____

_____

Nutritionists study people's diet by asking them to record a food diary.

When they've analysed the food diary they offer advice. This might be:

- change in diet
- nutrient supplements to prevent disease or treat disorders.

	Nutritional value for the day					
	Carbohydrate / g	Protein / g	Fat / g	Fibre / g	Sodium / g	Iron / mg
Dietary Reference Value (DRV)	300	50*	65	25	2.4	18

In pregnant women the DRV for protein is 60g and nursing mothers 65g

5   Suggest one reason why a nutritionist may suggest that a client

(a)   takes in more than the DRV

_____

_____

(b)   takes mineral supplements in addition to the DRVs in the table.

_____

_____

Note: DRV used to be called RDA. You may still see it written that way on packaging.

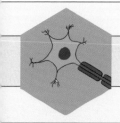

topic: nerves and hormones

1: Responding to our surroundings

It's very important that the environment *within* our bodies stays the same, even if outside conditions change.

The cells in our tissues and organs need stable conditions to work and survive.

It's the job of our nervous system and our endocrine (hormone) system to monitor and automatically control these conditions.

In a small group (or as your teacher directs) list conditions that need to be kept constant to keep your body working and healthy. Note which parts of your body help to do this.

_____

_____

_____

_____

_____

Check your list with other groups and add to it if you can.

Keeping the internal environment of the body constant is called **homeostasis**.

Part of this process involves responding to external changes that our senses detect. The next activities explore how they do this.

Write down the names of your five senses.

The five senses:

Receiving and sending messages

How does your body respond when it senses a change in the environment?

Impulse reactions are conscious and you can control them.

Reflex reactions are unconscious.

For example, if you're cold, you may put on a sweatshirt (an **impulse reaction**) or shiver (a **reflex reaction**).

List three more impulse and reflex reactions.

Impulse reactions	Reflex reactions
Putting on a sweatshirt when cold	*Shivering when cold*
_____	_____
_____	_____
_____	_____

Share your ideas. Add one more example of each type of reaction.

Speedy signals

The **central nervous system (CNS)** communicates by sending electrical signals through specialised cells called **neurones**. Its main parts are the brain and spinal cord.

There are three main types of neurone. Draw a line from each neurone to its function.

Sensory neurone   Carries signals through the CNS from sensory neurones to motor neurones

Relay neurone   Carries signals from sense organs to the brain and spinal cord

Motor neurones   Carries signals from the CNS to muscles and other responsive organs

Label these parts on the motor neurone diagram, right:

*   **Nucleus**

*   **Cytoplasm**

*   **Dendrites** *(branches which pick up signals from other neurones)*

*   **Axon** *(carries the signal to the nerve ending)*

*   **Sheath** *(covers the axon to prevent signals discharging in the wrong place)*

*   **Nerve ending** *(branched to make easy contact with other neurones or the effector organ)*

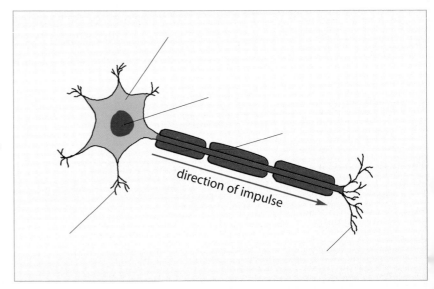

direction of impulse

2: Reflex arcs

Reflex arcs use the speed of the nervous system to give very rapid automatic responses. They do this by cutting out the thinking and using the smallest number of connections possible.

For example: if you touch a very hot object, your response is so fast you move your hand away before you even realise the object is hot - you move first, and shout *ouch!* afterwards.

Reflex arcs connect a **stimulus** (a change in the environment - external or internal) to a **response**.

Below is a reflex arc for the hot object example. Use these descriptions to complete the labels.

The first one - stimulus - has been done for you.

Passes signal through CNS

Arm bends and moves hand

~~Hot object~~

Takes signal to arm (effector muscles)

Touch receptors in skin

Takes signal to spinal cord (CNS)

Arm muscles contract

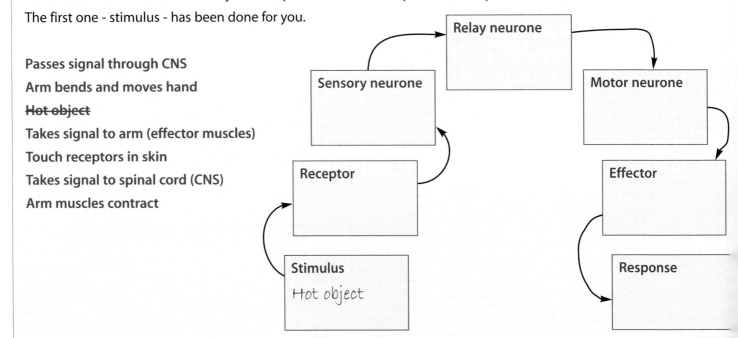

Sometimes the effector is a gland instead of a muscle. An example is sweat glands in the skin.

What other glands might need automatic control? Write some suggestions here.

_____

_____

3: Hot body? Cold body?

Your normal body temperature is about 37 °C. When you get hot, you start to sweat.

Your sweat glands produce a salty, watery solution that oozes out onto the surface of your skin.

The water evaporates into the air.

Changing a liquid to a gas requires a lot of energy. This removes heat from you and you cool down.

Try this experiment. Read it through. Collect the apparatus you'll need and set up your work space neatly.

Does sweating cool you down quickly?

Health and safety

A risk assessment must be carried out before starting work. Wear eye protection.

1   Place three test tubes (*mammals*) in a test tube rack.

2   Use tape or thread to cover two of them with cotton wool.

3   Thoroughly wet the cotton wool on one tube with water.

4   Pour hot water [CARE] into each tube up to the same level, about three-quarters full.

5   Place a thermometer into each tube.

6   In a suitable table, record the temperature / °C of each tube every two minutes for 15 minutes.

7   In your logbook or file, plot a graph of *temperature* on the *y*-axis against *time* on the *x*-axis.

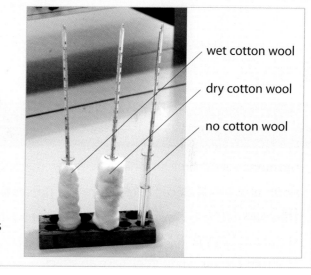

wet cotton wool

dry cotton wool

no cotton wool

Describe and explain the differences between the three *mammals*.

_____

_____

_____

Cooling the blood

Your nervous system also signals to increase the flow of blood to the capillaries in your skin. This is called **vasodilation** (it makes you look pink, or *flushed*). How does this help your body cool down?

_____

_____

Vasoconstriction is the reduction of blood flow to the capillaries in your skin. It makes you look pale.

When and why does your body do this?

_____

_____

Keep Your cool

Work in a pair to fill in the table below. Then get together with the rest of the class to compare notes.

What our bodies do when we're hot	What our bodies do when we're cold
_____	_____
_____	_____
_____	_____
_____	_____
_____	_____
_____	_____
_____	_____
_____	_____
_____	_____

4: Glucose in urine

Hormones are chemicals which affect how our body works. They are made by our **endocrine system**.

Hormones are produced in response to a stimulus.

They are used to control our growth and development.

Endocrine glands make the hormones. They secrete the hormones into the blood. The blood transports the hormones to **target organs** where they have an effect.

Get into a small group. What effects do hormones have on your bodies? Write a list below. Check with another group to see if they have any more ideas. Then as a class discuss this with your teacher.

_____

_____

_____

_____

_____

_____

Insulin

Insulin is a very important hormone as it controls blood glucose levels. Keeping blood glucose levels more or less constant is an important aspect of homeostasis.

Insulin (a protein) is made by the **pancreas**. When receptors in the pancreas detect that blood glucose levels are too high, the pancreas secretes insulin. Insulin makes your liver and muscles remove excess glucose then change it into glycogen for storage.

This is an example of **negative feedback**: the body detects a change and then reverses it. In this way conditions can be kept constant.

Insulin and Diabetes

It's estimated that diabetes affects at least 194 million people worldwide.

In a group, find out a bit more about diabetes by looking on some of these websites. Diabetes may be type 1 or type 2. Find out about type 1 only.

http://www.diabetes.org.uk/

http://www.dh.gov.uk/Home/fs/en (search for diabetes)

www.diabetesportal.com

http://www.idf.org/home/

http://www.diabetes.org/about-diabetes.jsp

www.diabetesmonitor.com/main.htm

www.diabetes-exercise.org

When you've done some reading fill in this table:

Type 1 diabetes (early onset)
Causes
Suggested treatment

Jenny has diabetes and uses insulin injections to help keep her blood glucose at safe levels.

She has just become a keen user of a gym.

Would you expect her to need more or less insulin each day?

Explain your answer.

_____

_____

Suggest why insulin is injected instead of taken in pills.

_____

Testing urine for glucose

The normal blood glucose level is 3.5 -7.5 mmol dm^{-3} (millimoles per cubic decimetre).

If the blood glucose level rises above 9.0 mmol dm^{-3} (for example if someone is suffering from diabetes), the body will get rid of the extra glucose in the urine.

Scientists have designed dipsticks called *Clinistix* which detect glucose in urine. *Clinistix* contain a colour-changing pad that is saturated with specific chemicals. These chemicals react with glucose.

Normal urine samples shouldn't contain glucose. If glucose is found in a urine specimen, a patient would be tested further.

You are going to investigate the use of *Clinistix*. First you will test solutions of known glucose concentration to see what colour change occurs. Then you'll test three patient samples of urine to see if any contain glucose.

Health and safety (for both procedures)

A risk assessment must be carried out before starting work.

Testing solutions of known glucose concentrations

1   You will have solutions of 0, 0.1, 1, 5, 10, 20 and 30 % glucose. Label 7 wells in the dimple tile for each solution. With a clean pipette each time, add a few drops of the correct stock sample to each well. (If you have a plain white tile, space out seven labels. Add a drop of solution by each label).

2   Dip a *Clinistix* test strip into the first solution. Observe the colour change. Record the colour in the table.

3   Using a new *Clinistix* test strip for each solution, test the other samples. (Note that there will be no difference in colour for some of the concentrations.)

Record your observations here:

Glucose concentration / %	Clinistix colour
0	_____
0.1	_____
1	_____
5	_____
10	_____
20	_____
30	_____

Testing urine samples for glucose content

1   Label three test tubes, one each for Karl, Sue and Peter.

2   With a clean pipette, add a small amount (about 5 cm^3) of urine sample to the relevant tube.

3   Dip a *Clinistix* test strip into the first sample. Observe the colour change. Read off the glucose range by comparing the strip with your calibration table.

4   Using a new *Clinistix* test strip for each sample, test the other samples.

Record your reults in the table.

	Karl	Sue	Peter
Colour change			
Approximate glucose concentration			
Is the person diabetic?			

The hormone system and nervous system

Summarise this section of your workbook. Tick the box to say whether each statement describes the nervous or the endocrine system.

	Nervous system	Endocrine (hormone) system
Information passes quickly as electrical impulses	☐	☐
Effects tend to be slower and much longer lasting	☐	☐
The signal spreads through the whole body	☐	☐
Information passes slowly as chemicals in the blood	☐	☐
Effects particular organs or parts of your body	☐	☐
The effect is quick and only lasts a few moments	☐	☐
Used to control blood glucose levels	☐	☐
Used to control movement of muscles	☐	☐

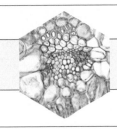

topic: cells

1: What are cells?

With your whole class, discuss "what is a cell?"

Label the two diagrams with these words. Think about the function of each part:

- Cell membrane
- ~~Nucleus~~
- Vacuole
- Cytoplasm
- Chloroplast
- Cell wall
- Mitochondria

Plant Cell

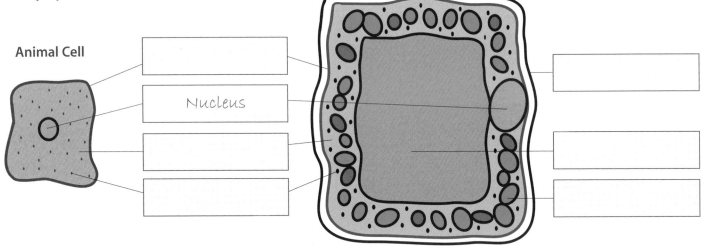

Animal Cell

Nucleus

Name three types of specialised cells. How are they specialised?

1 _____

2 _____

3 _____

Why do scientists study cells?

Cells are the basic building blocks of *all* living organisms.

Understanding how a cell works helps scientists understand the processes that go on inside organisms.

Cell cultures growing in sterile
bottles in a laboratory incubator

Photo: NASA

Cell biologists can grow (culture) cells artificially in the laboratory. These cells can then be studied to find out how they respond to different bio-chemicals, chemicals, drugs or conditions.

This has helped reduce animal testing - a lot of initial testing is now done on cell cultures before testing on animals.

A monkey at an
animal testing
laboratory

Think about the difference between one cell and a whole body full of cells. Suggest why cell cultures haven't totally replaced the need to do tests on animals.

_____

_____

_____

2: Inside a cell

Cell biologists look inside cells to find out how they work. By understanding what is normal they can recognise abnormal cells. Then they try to work out how to treat them.

Cells are so small, scientists have to use microscopes to see them.

You're going to make your own microscope slides and look at them under the microscope. The following procedure is for making a temporary mounted slide of human cheek cells. It can be adapted for producing a mounted slide of any suitable material.

Producing a mounted slide

Health and safety (for the next two procedures)

A risk assessment must be carried out before starting work. Wear eye protection. Biological material, especially of human origin should be handled with caution. **Under no circumstances** should you handle any cells taken or used by another student. Ensure that your own cell sample and slide is disposed of in disinfectant, as directed by your teacher.

Making a mounted slide of human cheek cells

Collect the equipment you need.

1   Take a cotton bud from a newly opened packet or a sterile swab.

2   Move the cotton bud over the inside of one cheek and along the outer lower side of the gum. This will remove cells from your mouth, even though you won't be able to see any.

3   Use a clean microscope slide. Smear the cotton bud over a small area of the centre of the slide. This transfers the cells.

4   Immediately put the used cotton bud into disinfectant in a container.

5   Pipette two or three drops of 1% methylene blue onto the smear. Cover with a coverslip.

6   If the whole of the coverslip doesn't have stain beneath it, you have used too little stain - start again.

If the stain is spreading out across the slide, you have used too much - use blotting tissue to remove the excess. (Take care: try not to soak up the stain from underneath the cover slip).

Try to avoid getting air bubbles between the microscope slide and coverslip.

7   Now use the standard procedure *Setting up a light microscope* to look at your slide under a microscope.

8   Draw some of the cells you can see. If you have a camera attached to the microscope take a picture.

9   When you have finished, put the slide and coverslip in a beaker of disinfectant. Your teacher or technician will dispose of this safely.

The next procedure shows you how to use a light microscope. Before starting, carefully read the procedure. Collect the equipment you need. The diagram will help you identify the various parts of your microscope.

Standard Procedure: Using a light microscope

Health and safety: A risk assessment must be carried out before starting work. Biological material should be handled with caution.

This procedure can be used to examine prepared samples mounted onto microscope slides. The light microscope uses objective lenses and an eyepiece. These magnify a sample so it can be seen clearly by the human eye.

1   If not self-illuminating, position the microscope so it has a good light source (but NOT direct sunlight). Use a lamp if necessary.

2   Rotate the nosepiece so the lowest power objective lens (shortest) is in position. Adjust the mirror, condenser and diaphragm. When you look down the eyepiece, the light should be bright and even.

3   Clip a prepared microscope slide onto the stage.

4   Use the coarse focus knob to lower the objective lens until it is close to the surface of the slide.

5   Look down the eyepiece and slowly turn the coarse focus knob. Move the lenses away from the slide, to bring the sample into focus.

6   Use the fine focus knob to get the sharpest view possible. Do this slowly, to avoid crushing the lens against the sample.

7   Examine the whole slide by moving the stage to view different parts.

8   To examine an area at higher magnification, position that point in the centre of the field of view. Change to the higher objective lens by turning the nosepiece. Focus the sample with the fine focus knob only.

Calculations

Calculate the final magnification of the microscope for each of the objective lenses on the microscope, using:

magnification (microscope) = magnification (eyepiece) x magnification (objective)

Diagram of a light microscope

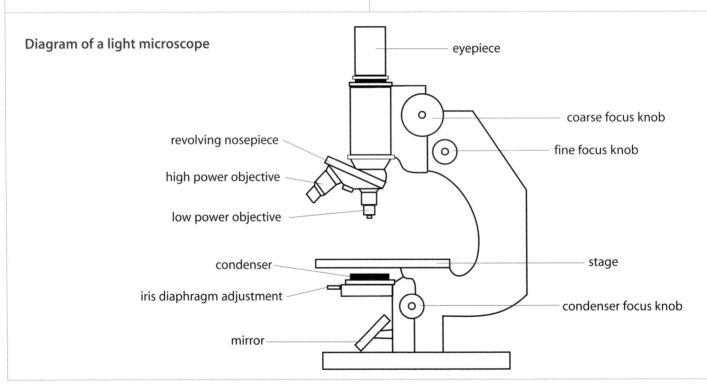

3: Transport in and out of cells

Diffusion

Fancy a cup of tea? Drop a tea bag in a mug and add boiling water. Leave it a couple of minutes and the water around the tea bag will turn brown. Chemicals in the tea move out of the bag and spread evenly through the water.

Diffusion takes place.

A chemical will move from a place where there's lots of it, to a place where there's not so much of it. The chemical moves from a **more concentrated** to a **less concentrated** place. This is diffusion.

Some materials move in and out of cells using this process. Pharmacologists work out the best way of getting drugs into the bloodstream often investigate diffusion.

When areas of different concentration exist, there is a **concentration gradient**. A chemical will diffuse until there isn't a concentration gradient any more. **Equilibrium** has been reached. There is an equal concentration throughout.

Find out about diffusion by trying this experiment. Read through the procedure and collect the equipment you need.

Pharmacologists often investigate diffusion

Investigating diffusion

Health and safety: A risk assessment must be carried out before starting work. Wear protective clothing.

1   Use the cork borer to make a well in the middle of the agar in the Petri dish.

2   Measure the diameter of the well with a ruler and write it on diagram 1.

3   Carefully fill the well with the red food colouring.

4   Leave the Petri dish for at least 30 minutes.

5   When you return, look at the Petri dish again. Draw the red area of the dish on diagram 2. Measure the diameter of the red area and write it in.

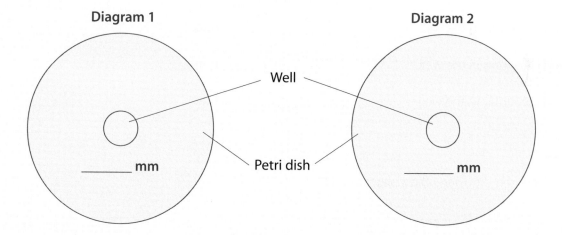

Questions

1   What differences are there between the diameter of the red area at the start and the end of the experiment?

_____

2   What has happened to the red food colouring during the experiment?

_____

3   What would happen to the agar in the Petri dish, if it were left for longer?

_____

4   When would the red food colouring stop diffusing through the agar?

_____

5   What do we say has happened to the red food colouring at this point?

_____

How quickly does diffusion happen?

Try this experiment, working in teams of five. Read through the procedure and collect the equipment you need.

Investigating diffusion

Health and safety

A risk assessment must be carried out before starting work.

Each team member:

Take a Petri dish and use the cork borer to make a well in the middle of the agar. Turn over your plate and label it.

(Team member 1 = Dish 1; Team member 2 = Dish 2, and so on.)

Team member:	Diameter of red circle after 30 minutes:
1: Put distilled water in the well.	_____ mm
2: Put 100% food colouring in the well.	_____ mm
3: Put 75% food colouring in the well.	_____ mm
4: Put 50% food colouring in the well.	_____ mm
5: Put 25% food colouring in the well.	_____ mm

Questions

1   In which dishes did diffusion take place?

_____

2   Water is colourless. How would you know diffusion took place in Dish 1?

_____

3   Does the concentration of food colouring effect the diameter of the red circle?

_____

4   Explain any differences you can see between the Petri dishes.

_____

_____

_____

5 Diffusion is a very important process.

In your library or resource centre, find out how diffusion is involved in gaseous exchange.

_____

_____

_____

_____

Osmosis

Living things are made up of cells.

Cells are sacks of chemicals held together by the cell membrane.

Simple chemicals and water are able to get in and out of cells through the pores in their membranes.

It's called a **partially permeable membrane**.

Water molecules are small enough to pass through partially permeable membranes.

Bigger molecules, such as sugar, are too large to pass. Water moves from a place where there's a lot of water (more **diluted**) to a place where there's less water (more **concentrated**). This movement of water is called **osmosis**.

The diagram, right, shows the direction of water movement, within a sugar solution, across a partially permeable membrane.

Find out about osmosis by trying the following experiment. Read through the procedure and collect the equipment you need.

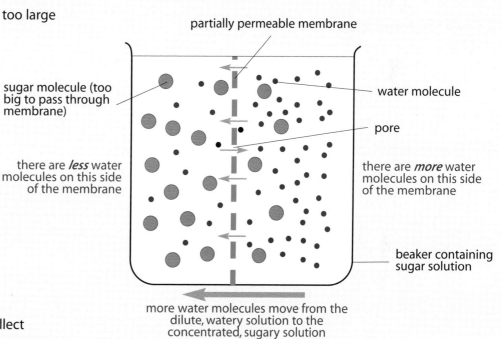

partially permeable membrane

sugar molecule (too big to pass through membrane)

water molecule

pore

there are *less* water molecules on this side of the membrane

there are *more* water molecules on this side of the membrane

beaker containing sugar solution

more water molecules move from the dilute, watery solution to the concentrated, sugary solution

Investigating osmosis

Health and safety

A risk assessment must be carried out before starting work. Wear protective clothing and eye protection.

1 Put three cucumber slices in a glass funnel and place the funnel in a conical flask.

2 Repeat step 1. You now have two flasks. Label one flask **no salt** and the other flask **salt**. (See photo.)

3 Use a spatula to sprinkle an even coating of salt onto the cucumber slices in the flask labelled **salt**.

4 Leave the flasks for 15 minutes.

NO SALT

SALT.

Record your observations.

_____

_____

_____

_____

Questions

1 What happened to the cucumber slices with salt on them?

_____

2 What happened to the cucumber slices without salt?

_____

3 Why were they different?

_____

4 Predict what would happen if you sprinkled sugar onto a bowl of strawberries.

_____

5 How might the food industry use the principles of osmosis?

_____

_____

_____

6 If there is time, find out how a kidney dialysis machine works.

_____

_____

_____

_____

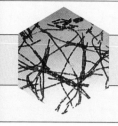

topic: the body under attack

1: Micro-organisms

List five diseases caused by micro-organisms.

_____

_____

Types of micro-organism

Micro-organisms are living organisms that can only be seen with a **microscope**.

Complete the table below. Some boxes have been filled in for you.

Plural	Viruses	Bacteria	Fungi
Singular	virus	bacterium	
Relative size		in between	Largest
Structure	smaller than a cell		single or multi-celled
Examples		E. coli	mushrooms, yeasts, moulds

Write the correct word to describe what the pictures show.

Choose from: **fungi • bacteria • virus**

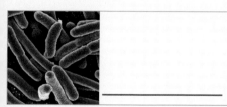 _____

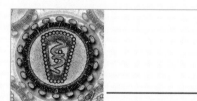 _____

 _____

Micro-organisms and disease

Some micro-organisms cause disease.

Draw a line to match up the diseases with the micro-organisms that cause them.

Disease	Micro-organisms
ring worm, athlete's foot	viruses
tuberculosis (TB), gonorrhea, whooping cough	fungi
measles, mumps, rubella, flu	bacteria

Explain how micro-organisms make us ill when they invade our bodies.

_____

_____

_____

Rapid multiplication

Once inside, bacteria can make us ill very quickly.

One reason is the speed at which they multiply.

They multiply by **asexual reproduction** (dividing in half).

Some bacteria can divide every nine minutes.

Complete the table to show how many bacteria there would be if they reproduce every 20 minutes.

Plot a graph of the results.

time / minutes	0	20	40	60	80	100	120
number of bacteria	1	2	4	___	___	___	___

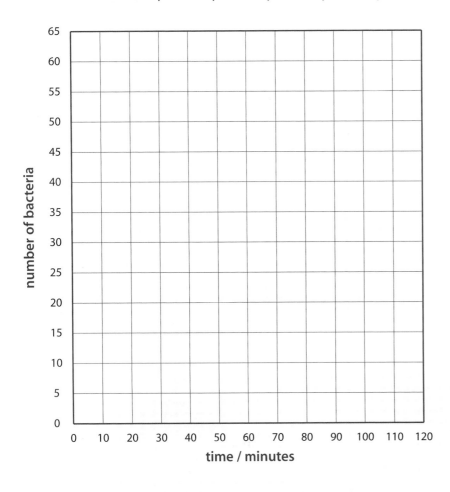

Fighting the invasion

If scientists want to find a treatment or cure for a disease caused by a micro-organism, what do they need to know?

_____

_____

_____

_____

_____

_____

2: Bacterial cultures

Techniques

Microbiologists study micro-organisms by culturing them (growing them) on **nutrient agar**. It's a jelly-like substance containing water and sugar.

To grow bacteria, a small quantity is put on the agar. This is called **inoculation**. One of the techniques microbiologists use for inoculating plates is called **streaking**.

When microbiologists culture bacteria they have to make sure other bacteria (for example, from the air or their hands) don't contaminate the agar plate. They only want to grow the one type of bacterium they're investigating. That's why they work in sterile conditions, using sterile equipment and **aseptic techniques**.

Four different types of nutrient agar that have been inoculated with bacteria 24 hours earlier

Working with agar plates

You will use two standard procedures:

* *Preparing nutrient agar plates*

* *Preparing streak cultures of bacteria*

Work in pairs. Each of you is going to pour two agar plates and streak them to culture colonies of bacterial cells.

Take it in turns to instruct one another step-by-step through the procedures.

Carry out the procedures quickly but carefully, to minimise risk of contamination.

Take care not to damage or tear the agar.

Health and safety (for both procedures)

A risk assessment must be carried out before starting work. Wear protective clothing and eye protection. Make sure your working area is clear and will allow you to work safely.

All micro-organisms in a sample multiply during incubation, including harmful ones. Therefore, after incubation samples MUST NOT be opened and must be disposed of safely [BIOHAZARD].

When you are not using a Bunsen burner, close its air hole so you can see a yellow flame. Keep it away from where you or others are working.

Standard procedure: Preparing nutrient agar plates

Equipment and materials

4 x sterile petri dishes • 4 x bottles of liquid agar kept in a water bath at 45 - 50 °C • Bunsen burner • permanent marker pen • paper towels

Procedure

1   Do not take the lids off the dishes. Turn the dishes over. Use a permanent marker pen to write your initials at the edge of the bottom of the dishes.

2   Collect a bottle of sterile liquid agar from the water bath and dry it with a paper towel.

3   Open the air hole of the Bunsen burner to turn it to a blue flame. Just above the blue flame is where the flame is hottest [CARE].

4   Loosen the cap of the bottle but do not open it.

5   If you are right handed, hold the bottle in your left hand and wrap the little finger of your right hand around the cap (if you are left handed use the opposite hand). Turn the bottle in your left hand to remove the cap. There is no need to keep the cap sterile because it is not being re-used. Put down the cap. Briefly pass the neck of the bottle through the hot part of the blue flame with your left hand.

6   With your right hand lift the lid of the petri dish slightly open, just enough to pour the liquid agar into the dish. Quickly but carefully pour the contents of the bottle into the dish and close the lid immediately.

7   Discard the empty agar bottle.

8   Gently rotate the dish to spread the agar evenly over the base of the Petri dish. Take care not to tip it, to reduce the chance of air bubbles.

9   Leave the Petri dish to cool and set. Take care not to disturb the dish while the agar is setting.

10 Repeat the procedure for the other three dishes.

The agar needs to set before you can streak it.

While you are waiting, work with your partner to answer these questions.

1   Underline the instructions in the procedure that helped you to reduce the risk of contamination.

2   Explain how each of the instructions you underlined helps to reduce risk of contamination.

_____

_____

_____

_____

3   Why does the agar need to contain sugar?

_____

_____

Standard procedure: Streaking cultures to produce colonies of bacteria

Equipment and materials

4 x pre-prepared agar plates • bottle of sterile water • inoculation loop • broth culture of a bacterium • Bunsen burner • permanent marker pen • masking tape or biohazard tape

Procedure

1   Open the air hole of the Bunsen burner to turn it to a blue flame. This is when it's hottest [CARE]. The air around the blue flame is sterile so try to work close to it.

2   Loosen the lid of the bottle containing a bacterial culture, but do not open it.

3   Hold the top of the inoculating loop like a pen in your right hand (or left hand if you are left handed). Move the end of the wire loop into the blue cone of the flame and slowly draw the loop up through the hot part of the flame. The wire and loop should glow red hot. Hold the loop next to the flame for a few seconds for it to cool down.

4   Wrap your little finger (of the hand holding the inoculating loop) around the lid of the bottle. Turn the base of the bottle with your other hand and remove the lid. Keep the inoculating loop still and close to the flame but do not allow it to go into the flame.

5   Pass the neck of the bottle briefly back and forth once through the hot part of the blue flame.

6   Dip the wire loop into the culture and remove a small sample. Pass the neck of the bottle back and forth once through the blue part of the flame again. Put the lid back on the bottle and put it down on the bench.

7   Lift the lid of the petri dish, keeping it above the agar plate Only lift the lid enough to put in the loop.

8   Move the loop forwards and backwards along the surface of the agar on one side of the plate to create an area containing a smeared sample. (see diagram 1 on the next page).

9   Turn the petri dish 90º anticlockwise. Look at diagram 2. Starting from point A, use the loop to make three streaks, spreading the sample to point B.

10   Make three streaks from point B to C (diagram 3) and three streaks from point C to point D, carrying the last streak into the centre of the agar (diagram 4). Remember to turn the plate through 90º each time. This should result in some single colonies growing on the plate. Replace the lid.

11   Flame and cool the loop as in step 3. Place the loop slowly into the flame, to avoid sputtering, then put it down.

12   Tape the lid to the base using four evenly-spaced short strips of sticky tape. DO NOT SEAL THE PLATE COMPLETELY. Turn the dish upside down.

13   Label around the edge of the base of the dish with: **the date, the name of the micro-organism** that you have streaked onto the plate.

14   Incubate the plate upside down at 25 ºC for 48 hours.

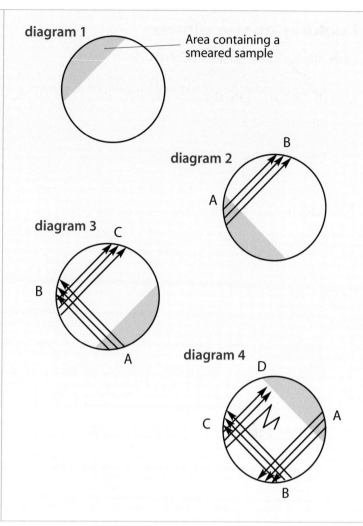

Now work with your partner to answer these questions.

1   Why is this technique used to isolate bacteria?

_____

2   Why did you have to heat the inoculating loop to red hot?

_____

_____

3   Why did you have to wait for the loop to cool before putting it into the culture?

_____

_____

4   Why did you prepare a plate with sterile water?

_____

_____

5   Why are the plates stored upside down?

_____

_____

Looking at the plates

Look at your streak plates. **DO NOT** open them.

1   Describe how the colonies of bacteria have grown.

_____

_____

_____

2   Why do you think they have grown like this?

_____

_____

_____

_____

3   Why is this technique useful when growing micro-organisms to study?

_____

_____

_____

_____

4   Look at the plate that you prepared with sterile water. Was your aseptic technique successful?
     If not, what may have gone wrong?

_____

_____

_____

_____

Disposing of waste

1   How will your plates be disposed of?

_____

_____

2   Why is it important that they are disposed of in this way?

_____

_____

3   What is this type of waste called?

_____

_____

3: Micro-organisms blown up

Microbiologists use microscopes to study micro-organisms.

Now you are going to prepare and look at two fungi.

You will be given:

• one agar slope of *Rhizopus* that has been prepared for you

• one agar slope of *Penicillium* that has been prepared for you.

Work with a partner to prepare microscope slides of each fungus from the agar slopes.

You should have practised using a microscope already ...

... but you might still want to refresh your memory.

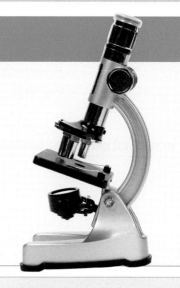

Health and safety

A risk assessment must be carried out for each procedure before starting work. Wear protective clothing and eye protection. Make sure your working area is clear and will allow you to work safely.

Read the procedure carefully and make sure you both understand what needs to be done. Collect the equipment and set up your Bunsen burner on a heat proof mat. When you're not using the Bunsen burner its air hole should be closed. The flame will be yellow.

You must work very carefully when near a lit Bunsen burner.

Standard procedure: Preparing microscope slides of micro-organisms

Equipment and materials

inoculating loop • distilled water • plastic dropping pipette • mounted needle • 2 x microscope slides • 2 x cover slips • 2 x small sticky labels • Bunsen burner • masking tape or biohazard tape

Procedure

1   Write your initials and the name of the sample being used on a small sticky label. Stick the label on one end of a microscope slide.

2   Add one drop of distilled water to the centre of the slide.

3   Loosen the lid of the bottle containing the fungal culture, but do not open it.

4   Hold the top of the inoculating loop like a pen in your right hand (or left hand if you are left handed). Move the end of the wire loop into the blue cone of the Bunsen flame and slowly draw the loop up through the hot part of the flame. The wire and loop should glow red hot. Hold the loop next to the flame for a few seconds for it to cool down.

5   Wrap your little finger (of the hand holding the inoculating loop) around the lid of the bottle.

Turn the base of the bottle with your other hand and remove the lid. Keep the inoculating loop still and close to the flame but do not allow it to go into the flame.

6   Pass the neck of the bottle briefly back and forth once through the hot part of the blue flame.

7   Gently run the inoculating loop across the surface of the agar slope and remove a small sample of fungus. Pass the neck of the bottle back and forth once through the blue part of the flame again. Put the lid back on the bottle and put it down on the bench.

8   Mix the sample of fungus into the drop of water on the slide.

9   Flame and cool the loop once more. Place the loop slowly into the flame, to avoid sputtering, then put it down.

10   Use a mounted needle to gently lower a cover slip over the sample.

11   Repeat steps 1 - 10 for the other fungus.

12   Look at both fungi under the microscope.

13   Use the space below to draw your observations of the two types of fungi. Label them with their name and the magnification that you were viewing them at. Do not use shading.

14   Follow your teacher's instructions about the disposal of your slides.

Your observations:

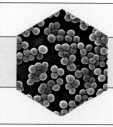

topic: germs and disease

1: Germs and disease

The immune system

Work in a small group. Discuss how micro-organisms get into the body and how the body defends itself from infection.

Collect ideas from other groups. Record your ideas in the space below.

Add labels of the structures that help defend the body from infection by micro-organisms. Write these in **blue**.

Describe how each of the structures you've labelled prevents infection. Write these below the labels in **red**.

_____

_____

_____

_____

_____

_____

_____

_____

_____

_____

_____

Getting help

Scientists have found ways to help the body's natural defences against infection.

Look at some products that are described as:

- antimicrobial (microbe is another name sometimes used instead of micro-organism)
- disinfectants
- antiseptics.

These might include soap, bleach, washing up liquid, *Dettol*, *TCP*, toothpaste, mouthwash, eye drops.

Look at the labels on the packaging to help you complete the table.

Name of product	How it protects against infection	Type of micro-organism(s) it protects against

Something to think about: what's the difference between an antiseptic and a disinfectant? Discuss the question with one or two other students in your class and write down your ideas.

_____

_____

_____

2: Blood defences

What's blood made of?

Look back at page 11 of this workbook to remind yourself what blood is made of. Different components of blood help defend the body in different ways.

Their jobs

Platelets help to clot the blood and form scabs to prevent infection when you cut yourself.

Number these sentences to give the correct order for how a scab is formed.

_____ *Fibrin forms a mesh that traps blood cells.*

_____ *The skin is broken and blood is exposed to the air.*

_____ *The mesh of fibrin and blood cells dries to become a clot (scab).*

_____ *Platelets cause fibrinogen to form fibrin (thin threads).*

Phagocytes destroy micro-organisms.

Draw and annotate a diagram to show how they do it.

Complete the following paragraph using these missing words:

immune • lymphocytes • antibodies • micro -organism • destroy • antigen • recognise

If a disease-causing_____ enters the blood, white blood cells called _____ recognise the

micro-organism as foreign (something not made in the body).

The foreign substance on the surface of the micro-organism is called the _____.

Lymphocytes produce proteins called _____ which bind to foreign particles.

This identifies the particles as a target to _____. The antibodies have to specifically bind to one type of

micro-organism. Making lots of specific antibodies can take a week. It's why you feel ill during this time.

After the micro-organism is killed, some of the specific antibodies remain. So, if the same micro-organism invades

the body again, the immune system can _____ and kill it more quickly.

This means you are_____ to that micro-organism.

When a micro-organism is first encountered, the white blood cells take some time to make the correct antibodies.
Explain why you become ill during this time.

_____

_____

_____

Sarah has chicken pox. Her brother David has never had chicken pox. Their mother tells David to stay away from Sarah.
Explain in detail why David's mother thinks her children should stay apart.
Include the words **antigens, antibodies, contagious** and **immune**.

_____

_____

_____

David doesn't listen to his mother and catches chicken pox from Sarah.

Sarah asks if she should stay away from David.

Write an explanation to Sarah telling her what she should do.

Your explanation should include the words **antigens, antibodies, lymphocytes** and **immune**.

A child with chicken pox

_____

_____

_____

_____

_____

Suggest why it was actually good that David caught chicken pox as a child.

_____

_____

_____

_____

3: Vaccinations

List the diseases you think you've had a vaccination against.

_____

_____

_____

Explain how a vaccine brings about immunity. Use the key words: **antigens, immune, phagocytes, lymphocytes** and **antibodies**.

_____

_____

_____

_____

_____

The MMR vaccination has been in the news. What do you know about this?

_____

_____

_____

Evidence of effectiveness

Look at the graph below.

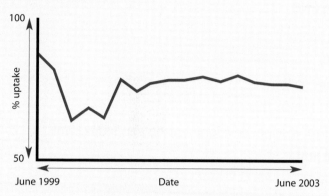

Take up of the MMR vaccination in England between June 1999 and June 2003

What does the graph tell you?

_____

_____

_____

There is some evidence that more children are getting measles.

Suggest a possible reason for this.

_____

_____

_____

Advice for parents

The NHS is concerned that fewer children are being vaccinated for MMR, Tuberculosis (TB) and polio.

They have asked you to design an information leaflet for parents.

The leaflet will be distributed in pharmacies and doctor's surgeries. It will need to stand out from the other leaflets.

1   Choose which vaccine (MMR, TB or Polio) to produce a leaflet for.

2   Research your chosen area. The websites listed on the next page may help.

3   Go to doctors' surgeries and pharmacies to see what leaflets already exist.

Your leaflet must be factual and aimed at parents. It should include information about:

•   the disease the vaccine is for

•   the effects of the disease

•   what the vaccine is

•   any possible side effects and their likelihood

•   the importance of being vaccinated.

Your leaflet will be assessed on it's content, accessibility and design.

Some useful websites

These might be good places to start your research.

MMR	http://www.medinfo.co.uk/immunisations/mmr.html
	http://www.mmrthefacts.nhs.uk/
	http://news.bbc.co.uk/1/hi/health/3640898.stm
	http://www.cdc.gov/nip/publications/VIS/vis-mmr.pdf
TB	http://www.aeras.org/
	http://www.who.int/vaccine_research/diseases/tb/vaccine_development/bcg/en/index.html
	http://www.metrokc.gov/health/tb/bcgvaccine.htm
	http://www.travelhealth.co.uk/diseases/bcg.htm
Polio	http://www.cdc.gov/nip/publications/VIS/vis-IPV.pdf
	http://www.accessexcellence.org/AE/AEC/CC/polio.html
	http://familydoctor.org/333.xml
	http://www.medinfo.co.uk/immunisations/polio.html

4: Protection against micro-organisms

You will investigate the effectiveness of antiseptics and disinfectants.

Work in a group to compare different products that can be bought in the shops.

Within your group, work with a partner. Share the products between you.

At the end of the investigation, compare your results and decide which was the most effective.

Read the standard procedure carefully, before you go any further.

The thinking before the doing

What will you measure to say how effective the antiseptic or disinfectant was?

_____

Which conditions must be the same in each experiment to be sure:

- any change in bacterial growth is due to the antiseptic or disinfectant being used
- that your conclusions will be valid?

_____

_____

_____

Now answer these questions

1   List how you will ensure that your procedure uses aseptic techniques.

_____

_____

2   Why will you add distilled water to one plate?

_____

3   What difference do you predict you'll see, after the plates have been incubated for a few days?

_____

4   Justify your prediction.

_____

_____

_____

5   Other than the effectiveness, what other tests do you think should be carried out before antiseptics and disinfectants are sold?

_____

_____

6   Why is it important that scientists test the antiseptics and disinfectants, before they go on sale?

_____

_____

Health and safety

Complete the following risk assessment for your investigation. (Your teacher should check it before you start the practical work.) In each box write:

The activities/chemicals • The associated hazards • The safety precautions you've put in place

If you're using chemicals, tick the box when you've read the relevant CLEAPSS information.

Wear protective clothing and eye protection. Make sure your work area is clear and will allow you to work safely.

Investigating chemicals that protect against micro-organisms

Equipment and materials

4 x petri dishes containing agar seeded with bacteria [BIOHAZARD] • permanent marker • different antiseptic and disinfectant solutions • distilled water • pair of metal forceps • filter paper discs (made with stationery hole punch) • Bunsen burner • biohazard tape

Procedure

1   Collect the equipment you need. Set up a Bunsen burner on a heatproof mat.

   When you are working in aseptic conditions the air hole of the Bunsen burner should be open and the flame blue. Work close to the flame. When you are not using the Bunsen burner, the air hole should be closed and the flame yellow.

2   Label the bottom of the four Petri dishes that have been spread with bacteria [BIOHAZARD].

   Label one plate **water** and the other three plates with the names of the antiseptics or disinfectants used.

3   Use the metal forceps to pick up a filter paper disc. Dip it into the bottle of distilled water. Drain the filter paper on the side of the bottle until it stops dripping.

4   Quickly but carefully lift the lid of the Petri dish just enough to allow you access and put the filter paper disc in the centre of the dish. Use the metal forceps to press the disc down gently. Take care not to damage the agar.

5   Briefly pass the metal forceps through the Bunsen burner flame to kill any bacteria that might have been picked up from the surface of the agar plate. Allow them to cool.

5   Repeat steps 3 and 4 for the three antiseptics or disinfectants you're investigating. Think about how you will make sure that you don't contaminate any of the plates with the previous sample used.

6   Fasten the Petri dish lid with four short strips of biohazard tape. Incubate your plates at 25 °C for two days.

In the next lesson ...

Look at the agar plates you prepared. DO NOT OPEN THEM.

Draw what you see on your agar plates on the diagrams below.

Sample added: None (water only)

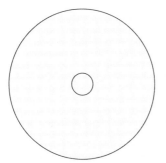

Sample added: _____

Sample added: _____

Sample added: _____

Measure the average diameter of clear zone (**inhibition zone**) around the sample, in mm, for each plate. Calculate the area. Complete the table.

	Area of no bacteria growth (inhibition zone) / mm^2
Water	

Coming to a conclusion

Collect the results from people who used other antiseptics or disinfectants.

Write the names of the products in decreasing order of effectiveness.

_____

_____

_____

_____

_____

Evaluating the investigation

Was there anything that you did during the procedure that could have affected the validity of the results?

_____

_____

_____

How do you think each of these errors could be overcome, if you were to repeat this investigation?

_____

_____

_____

What else could you do to improve the validity of your results?

_____

_____

_____

How could you extend this investigation to help reinforce your conclusion?

_____

_____

_____

topic: drugs - helpful and harmful

1: Useful drugs and testing new drugs

Take your medicine

Think about medicines.

1   Can you name any? _____

2   What are they for? _____

3   What type of drug are they (e.g. antibiotic, pain relief)?

_____

4   Does the medicine cure the illness or treat the symptoms of the illness?

_____

5   Which drugs are:

a   Bought at a pharmacists without a prescription?_____

These are called over-the-counter (OTC) medicines.

b   Prescribed by a doctor? _____

Patient information

You'll be given examples of medicine packaging and patient information leaflets.

Work in a small team (two or three of you) to complete this table.

Illness or disease	Type of drug	Name of drug	Cure or relief	OTC or prescription

Before you take your medicine

Continue working in your small group.

Try to answer these questions.

1   Before you take medicine, what information do you **need** to know?

_____

_____

_____

2   What other information would you like to know about a medicine, before you take it?

_____

_____

3   Why is it important that the patient information leaflet includes information for children and babies?

_____

4   Why is it important that the patient information leaflet includes information for pregnant women?

_____

5   How do scientists find out the information needed by patients when taking a medicine?

You'll discuss this question in class. As you do, make notes in the boxes below:

Testing new medicines on cells (*in vitro*)

↓

Testing new medicines on animals (*in vivo*)

↓

Clinical trials

For each of the statements below mark with a cross on the arrow to indicate how strongly you agree or disagree with the statement.

Testing on cells is a waste of time as it won't give any information about the medicine

Strongly disagree   Strongly agree

Testing on animals should be illegal

Strongly disagree   Strongly agree

Clinical trials should be carried out from the start of testing a new medicine

Strongly disagree   Strongly agree

2: Antibiotics

Superbugs

An article from www.guardian.co.uk in February 2006 carried the headline:

Superbug deaths up by nearly a quarter in year

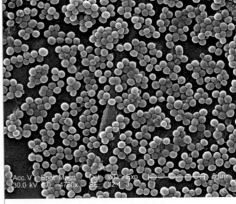

An electron micrograph of the MRSA superbug

The piece, by Polly Curtis, a Guardian health correspondent, quoted figures from the Office for National Statistics.

Their latest figures showed that occurences of MRSA - dubbed the hospital superbug - had increased by almost a quarter in one year.

The article claimed that MRSA is *"six times more likely to be a factor in the deaths of people in NHS hospitals than anywhere else."*

More than one thousand people *"had MRSA recorded on their death certificate as a principle cause of death or a contributory factor in 2004, a rise of 213 from 2003."*

More about micro-organisms

Is some of the increase down to an increased resistance to antibiotics? Or, is hospital hygiene playing a part? MRSA, or methicillin-resistant *Staphylococcus aureus*, is one of a group of bacteria which cause difficult-to-treat infections. They are resistant to standard antibiotics.

Go to the website **www.microbe.org**

1   Click on the globe labelled *Join Sam in solving microbe mysteries*

2   Click on *Case #6: Virus or bacterium?*

3   Read through the information and complete the table.

	Bacteria	Viruses
Size		
Structure		
Diagram		
Method of reproduction		

4   Click *Case #2: An evolutionary success*.

5   Scroll to the bottom

6   Click *Genetic changes, or mutations*.

7   What are antibiotics?

_____

_____

8   Create a flow chart below to explain how bacteria become resistant to antibiotics.

9   If you are suffering from a cold, should you ask for antibiotics from your doctor? Explain your answer.

_____

_____

10   Why is it so important that people on antibiotics complete the entire course?

_____

_____

3: Fact not fiction - recreational drugs

Drugs are chemicals which affect the body.

Some effects are beneficial. For example, relieving pain or reducing inflammation.

Some effects are harmful. For example, causing high blood pressure or liver damage.

Not all drugs have medicinal uses. Some drugs are used by people for so-called recreational purposes. Sometimes this has severe consequences.

In 30 seconds list as many legal and illegal drugs as you can think of:

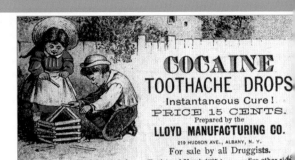

Before the harmful effects were known, cocaine was used, legally, as a pain-killer in a number of different products.

Legal drugs	Illegal drugs
_____	_____
_____	_____
_____	_____
_____	_____
_____	_____
_____	_____

Why do you think the drugs in the legal column are legal and the drugs in the illegal column are illegal?

_____

_____

Are there any drugs in your list that you feel should be made legal or illegal? Explain your answer.

_____

_____

_____

_____

Is it important that people are informed about both legal and illegal drugs? Explain your answer.

_____

_____

_____

_____

What sort of information do people need to know about drugs?

_____

_____

_____

_____

_____

Where can students go for this information?

_____

_____

_____

_____

Scientists Working - contributions wanted

Write a short article for a magazine.

The magazine is called *Scientists Working*. It's intended to be read by 15 year-olds.

The article should be around 300 words and give an objective and unbiased overview of the issues involving drugs.

You can choose your own title.

Make sure you:

- write scientifically, using correct terminology and facts, with your audience in mind

- plan your article before you start writing, e.g. subheadings, information in each section, sections in a logical order.

You should include:

- information about recreational drugs, such as nicotine, alcohol, antidepressants, amphetamines, barbiturates, heroin, cocaine

    - are they legal or illegal?

    - can the use of them lead to addiction? If so why?

    - what affects do they have on the body?

- Tobacco smoke contains nicotine, tar and carbon monoxide

    - what are the effects of each of these ingredients on the body, in particular the respiratory and circulatory systems?

- Alcohol

    - how does alcohol affect the nervous system in the short term?

    - what are the long term effects of alcohol abuse on the liver and brain?

Photos, top to bottom:

Black tar heroin; A dried bud from the *Cannabis sativa* plant; Crack cocaine; A farmer tending to his tobacco plants.

4: Detecting drugs

Detecting alcohol

The original *Breathalyzer* contained a glass tube of orange/yellow crystals.

These turned green when alcohol vapour was blown over them. The more alcohol, the further the green colour spread.

What was the purpose of the *Breathalyzer*?

_____

What is the chemical name for the alcohol in alcoholic drinks?

_____

The colour change is caused by a chemical reaction.

Try it yourself. Work with a partner. You'll be given samples of:

ethanol • ethanoic acid • propan-1-ol • propanone

Testing for alcohol

Health and safety

A risk assessment must be carried out for each procedure before starting work. Wear eye protection.
Ethanol, propan-1-ol, propanone and ethanoic acid are HIGHLY FLAMMABLE and IRRITANTS, so take care.

Method [to be carried out in a fume cupboard]

For each sample in turn:

1   In a test tube, mix 2 cm^3 of dilute sulfuric acid [IRRITANT] and 2 cm^3 potassium dichromate solution [TOXIC].

2   Add two drops of the sample. Shake gently to mix.

3   If there is no visible reaction, warm gently in a water bath at 30 $^{\circ}$C. Do not use a naked flame.

Findings

A colour change from yellow to green or blue indicates a positive result.

Say which sample(s) gave a positive test.

_____

_____

Drugs have fingerprints

A man is found unconscious at home. Nearby is some white powder - perhaps a harmful drug or a pain-killer.

Maybe the man has taken an over-dose.

Doctors need to identify the powder as soon as possible. Then they can give the correct treatment.

Suggest two other situations when scientists need to identify an unknown chemical.

_____

_____

Analytical scientists use various techniques. One is **infrared spectroscopy**.
It takes only a short time to identify an organic compound by this method.

How infrared (IR) spectroscopy works

Organic compounds absorb infrared radiation. Different types of bonds in them absorb different wavelengths.

The instrument produces an **infrared spectrum** - a graph showing which wavelengths the sample absorbs.

This tells us which types of bonds the compound contains.

No two compounds have exactly the same arrangement of bonds, so each has its own infrared spectrum.

Like fingerprints, the spectrum can be used to identify the compound.

Look at these infrared spectra of two simple hydrocarbons.

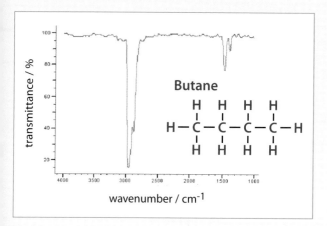

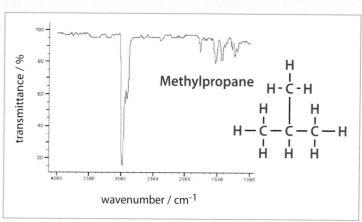

Why are the spectra similar, but not quite the same?

_____

_____

Notice that the peaks are upside down. This is because bonds *absorb* the infrared, so there's a drop in the amount passing through the sample.

Interpreting infrared spectra

The main peaks in the spectra above are due to carbon-hydrogen (C-H) bonds. Other bonds absorb at different wavenumbers. Here are some examples.

Wavenumber / cm^{-1}	3200-3750 (wide peak)	3150-3500	2500-3300 (wide peak)	2800-3100	1650-1750	1300-1500	1000-1300
Bond type	O-H (not in -COOH)	N-H	O-H (in -COOH)	C-H	C=O	C-H	C-O

Using this table, decide which bonds produce peaks A to D in the spectrum for ethanol, C_2H_5OH.

A _____

B _____

C _____

D _____

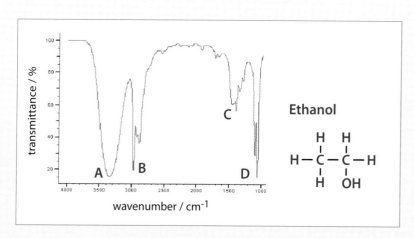

Now look at the spectra for two common analgesics (pain killers): aspirin and paracetamol.

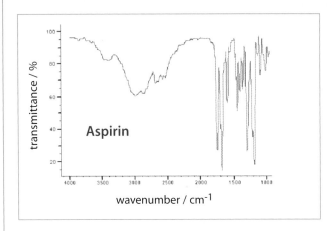

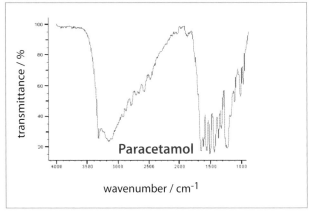

1   Which one contains an organic acid (-COOH) group? _____

Label this peak **X** on the appropriate spectrum.

2   Which contains an N-H bond and an O-H bond but no -COOH group? _____

Label these two peaks **Y** (for N-H) and **Z** (for O-H).

3   Explain why the aspirin spectrum has two peaks between 1650 and 1750.

_____

Infrared fingerprints

Here is the infrared spectrum of the white powder found near the unconscious man.

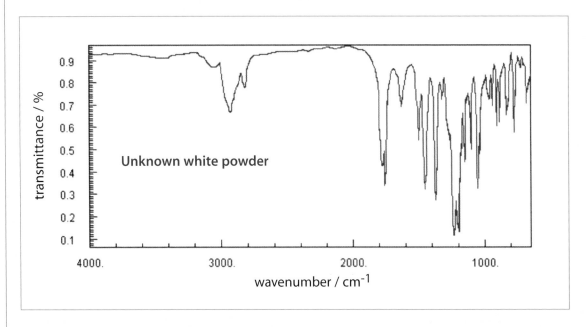

Compare this with the spectra of aspirin, paracetamol, and the three drugs shown on *Datasheet: Published infrared spectra* (on the next page).

The details in a spectrum depend on the spectrometer used and the purity of the sample.

Which spectrum matches the unknown most closely?

_____

Datasheet: Infrared spectra of three addictive drugs

Cocaine

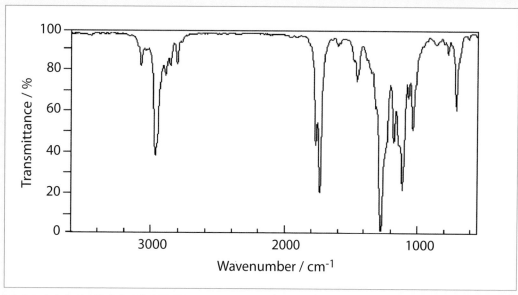

Heroin

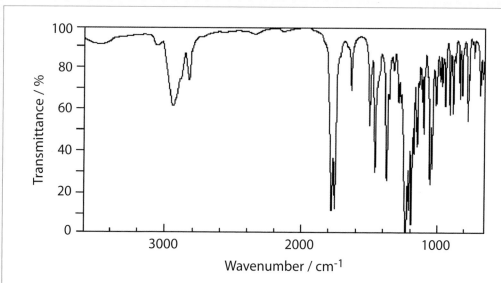

Morphine

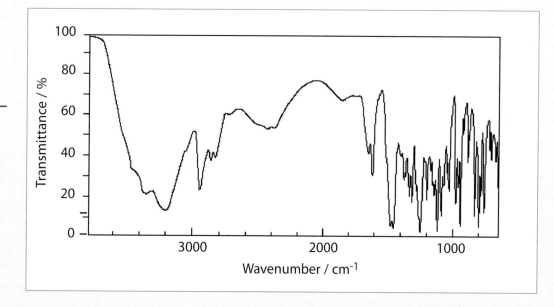

Notes

Notes

Fourth Impression, 2009